Make-Believe Time

Senior Author
John A. McInnes

Associate Authors
Margaret Gerrard
Judith Lawrence
John Ryckman

Contents

Mr. and Mrs. Impossible

Mrs. Impossible
Went to the shop
And bought a new hat
With
  a
    fish
      on
        the
          top.

But on her way home,
She was stopped by a cat
Who said, "Give me that fish
On the top of your hat."

So
away
went
Mrs. Impossible.

Mr. Impossible
Went to the shop
And bought a new hat
With
  a
    snow-
      man
        on
          top.

But when he went out
For a walk in the sun,
The snowman got hot
And it started to run.

So
away
went
Mr. Impossible.

5

Mrs. Impossible
Went to the shop
And bought a new hat
With a feather on top.

But on her way home
She stopped at the zoo
To talk to the birds
And the big kangaroo.

She looked at the bear
And the elephant too.
She tickled the elephant,
And he said, "Kerchoo!"

So
away
went
Mrs. Impossible.

Mr. Impossible
Went to the shop
And bought a new hat
With a chimney on top.

A big bird was sitting
Way up in a tree.
"I don't want to live
In this tree-top," said she.

She looked at the hat
And said, "What do I see?
What a good place for nesting
That chimney would be."

So
away
went
Mr. Impossible.

Mrs. Impossible
Went to the shop.
She got a new hat
With a rocket on top.

Then Mr. Impossible
Went to the shop.
He, too, got a hat
With a rocket on top.

Pop! Bang! Whizzzz!

And
away
went
Mr. and Mrs. Impossible.

John McInnes

The Old Man's Mitten

Long ago, on a cold winter morning, an old man was walking along in the forest. He stopped to pick up some sticks for firewood. As he did so, he dropped one of his mittens. He walked on through the forest.

After a time, a mouse came along. She saw the mitten in the snow.

"Oh," she said to herself, "here is just the thing for me. I could live happily in this mitten until spring." Into the mitten she went.

Soon a little white rabbit came through the forest. He looked at the mitten, too. "Hello," he called. "Who lives in this mitten?"

"I do," said the mouse.

"Who are you?" asked the rabbit.

"I am Crunch-Munch the Mouse," answered the mouse. "Who are you?"

"I am Fleet-Feet the Rabbit, and I am looking for a place to live," said the rabbit. "May I live in this mitten with you?"

"Yes, you may," said Crunch-Munch. "I will move over."

Crunch-Munch moved over, and Fleet-Feet moved in beside her. Now there were two animals in the mitten.

After a time, a frog came hopping along. "Hello," she called. "Who is in this mitten?"

"We are," answered the animals. "Crunch-Munch the Mouse and Fleet-Feet the Rabbit. Who are you?"

"I am Hop-Stop the Frog, and I am looking for a place to live," said the frog. "Do you have room for me in this mitten?"

"Yes," said Crunch-Munch and Fleet-Feet. "There is room for you, too."

So Crunch-Munch and Fleet-Feet moved over, and Hop-Stop the Frog moved in. The three animals lived happily in the mitten.

Soon, along came a red fox. He looked into the mitten. "Hello," he said. "Who is in this mitten?"

"We are," shouted the three animals. "Crunch-Munch the Mouse, Fleet-Feet the Rabbit, and Hop-Stop the Frog. Who are you?"

"I am Red-Head the Fox," said the fox. "Please move over and make room for me."

"Come in," answered the animals. "The mitten will hold one more."

So the mouse, the rabbit, and the frog moved over until there was room for Red-Head the Fox to move in. Then the four animals lived happily in the mitten.

After a time, a black bear came along. "What a big mitten!" she said to herself. "I would like to sleep in here." She put her nose into the mitten. "Who lives here?" she asked.

"We do," cried all the animals in the mitten. "Who are you?"

"I am Black-Back the Bear," she answered, "and I want to come in."

"No room! No room!" called the animals in the mitten. "There is no room for you. This mitten will hold no more. It is full."

"Please move over and try to make room," said Black-Back the Bear.

"We will try," said all the animals.

Crunch-Munch, Fleet-Feet, Hop-Stop, and Red-Head moved over, and Black-Back moved in. Now there were five animals in the mitten.

Soon the old man went back to the forest to look for his mitten. He looked and looked, but he could not find it. "I'll have to make myself a new mitten," he said.

So the old man went home and made himself a new mitten. And Crunch-Munch, Fleet-Feet, Hop-Stop, Red-Head, and Black-Back lived happily for a long time in the mitten in the forest.

They may be living there still.

Summer at Rocky Point

The Lighthouse

    Slip, slap! Slip, slap! The sound of the windshield wipers made Jimmy Carson sleepy. He rubbed his eyes and stretched to keep himself awake.

    "Are we almost there, Mom?" he asked. "We've been driving for nearly three hours."

"Yes, sleepyhead," his mother answered. "When we get to the top of the next big hill you'll see Rocky Point. Keep your eyes open and you'll see the sign."

"What's it like at Rocky Point?" asked Jimmy.

"You'll see," said his mother. "It's going to be fun spending the summer by the sea. Maybe some of your friends will come and visit us."

"I hope so," said Jimmy. "I hope Terry comes. He's my best friend. His uncle has a new boat. He's going to sail along the coast this summer, and Terry is going with him."

"They could stop and visit us," said Mrs. Carson.

Jimmy looked around at his baby sister. She was sleeping in her basket in the back seat of the car.

"Nancy seems to like long car rides," he said.

"When she wakes up she'll want her bottle," said Mrs. Carson. "You can give it to her."

"I wonder what Dad is doing right now," said Jimmy.

"When I phoned your dad this morning, he was painting the house and making a new sign for the store," said Mrs. Carson.

"I hope he's getting supper ready," said Jimmy. "I'm getting hungry."

"We're almost there," said his mother. "There's the sign for the Rocky Point Lookout. Everybody stops there to see the view."

Mrs. Carson slowed the car down and pulled over to the side of the road.

Just then, the rain stopped and the sun peeked through the clouds. From the top of the hill, Rocky Point looked like a toy village. The little white houses were huddled together. Their roofs were splashes of colour beside the grey sea.

"What a neat little village!" said Jimmy. "It looks as if all the houses are getting ready to jump into the sea. And there's the old lighthouse!"

"Our house is right beside the lighthouse," said Mrs. Carson. "The store is in the lighthouse."

"That must be a funny store," said Jimmy.

They drove down the hill and through the village. In a few minutes they pulled up in front of the summer house. Jimmy got out and held the car door open. His mother lifted out the baby in the basket. They went into the house.

"We're here, Dad," called Jimmy.

His dad came out of the kitchen.

"Hi, Jimmy! Hi, Margaret! Hi, big girl!" He picked up Nancy and gave her a kiss. She started to cry.

"Hello, Brad," said Margaret Carson. "Nancy slept all the way here. She must be hungry. I think she wants her bottle."

"I'll give it to her," said Jimmy. "What's for supper, Dad?"

"Fried clams," answered Brad. "I went clam digging when the tide went out today."

"I love clams," said Jimmy, "and you know how to cook them."

"The new sign on the store looks great," said Margaret. "You've been busy."

"The store is nearly finished," said Brad. "It's surprising how you can make an old lighthouse into a store. The ground floor is where we'll do the selling. There's a small room upstairs for storing things."

"I can't wait to see it," said Margaret, "but I guess we'd better get at those clams. Jimmy's starving."

While they were eating supper, Jimmy asked a lot of questions about the lighthouse. "Are you going to let people go to the top of the lighthouse," he asked.

"No," answered his dad. "There's not much room up there, but I'll take you up. We'll go before sundown. There aren't any lights in the store yet. The men are coming Monday to put them in."

"Is it scary in the lighthouse?" asked Jimmy.

"Sometimes," answered his father. "It's old and creaky."

"It's the oldest lighthouse around here. That's why so many people come to see it," said Margaret to Jimmy. "My grandfather was the lighthouse keeper here a long time ago."

"The lighthouse was built over a hundred years ago," said Brad. "It was a very important lighthouse. The big sailing ships used to sail right by here on their way up the coast."

After supper they all went to the lighthouse. Jimmy ran ahead. The big old door creaked as he pushed it open. Inside, the store was one big round room with small windows. There were stairs that led to the top of the lighthouse.

"It doesn't look much like a store," said Jimmy.

"Not yet," said his dad. "There's still some work to do on it yet."

"I'll help you," said Jimmy. "Look at the stairs, Mom. They go round and round, and up and up."

"Why don't you and your dad go round and round and up and up," said his mother. "I know you both want to. I'll take Nancy back to the house and put her to bed."

Brad Carson took the flashlight that hung inside the door. He and Jimmy went up the stairs. It got darker and darker as they went up.

"It's scary up here," said Jimmy. He reached out for his father's hand and squeezed it tightly.

"I got a real scare the first time I came up," said Jimmy's dad. "Something flew out at me in the dark. At first I didn't know what it could be. It was a bat that was living up here."

"I bet you scared the bat, too," said Jimmy.

When they got to the top of the lighthouse, Jimmy looked out the window.

"It's a long way down, Dad," he said. "Look at all the sharp rocks. There's a big boat out there."

"Yes," said his dad. "I think it's an oil tanker. There are some fishing boats, too."

Jimmy's dad showed him the lighthouse lamp. He said, "This is the lamp your great-grandfather used when he worked here. He had to light this lamp every evening at sundown."

"It's a small lamp for such a big lighthouse," laughed Jimmy.

"Yes," said his dad, "but the glass made it look bigger. The men on the boats could see it from far away. Every morning the lighthouse keeper climbed the stairs to the top of the lighthouse. He opened the glass and turned out the lamp. Then he cleaned the glass and made it shine. After that, he cleaned all the windows."

"Those rocks look dangerous," said Jimmy.

"Yes," answered Brad. "There was a shipwreck on those rocks years ago. A big sailing ship crashed into the rocks and sand. No one knows how it happened."

When Jimmy and his dad got back to the house, Margaret showed Jimmy some of the things they were going to sell in the store. There were rugs that people in the village made. There were pictures made out of shells, and there was a ship's bell. When Jimmy rang it, Nancy woke up.

"Oops! Sorry," said Jimmy.

"Here's a ship in a bottle," said Margaret. "But it's not for sale. My grandfather made it for me."

"I wonder if the ship that got wrecked looked like this ship in the bottle," said Jimmy.

"It might have," said his dad.

"I'd like to take the boat to my room," said Jimmy. "I want to look at it some more before I go to sleep."

"Maybe you'll dream about sailing ships and lighthouses and shipwrecks," said his dad.

"And treasures," said Jimmy.

He carried the ship in the bottle carefully to his room. He looked at it for a long time before he went to sleep.

The next week was a busy one for everybody. The workmen finished their work and left. The Carsons worked quickly to get the store ready to open. There were boxes to unpack and shelves to fill. When the store opened they were busier than ever.

Jimmy got a chance to do all kinds of things. He helped his dad and mother in the store. He looked after Nancy. Sometimes he walked down into the village to do the shopping. He talked to the visitors and showed them around Rocky Point. He liked answering questions about the lighthouse. He was very happy.

Some mornings the store wasn't very busy. Then Jimmy and his dad or mother had some time off. They went swimming or fishing, or just walking along the shore. Jimmy found some beautiful sea shells.

One morning Jimmy got a letter from his friend, Terry. Jimmy read the letter to his mother.

"I'm glad Terry is coming to see us," she said. "Maybe his uncle will take us for a ride in his new boat."

"I hope they get here tomorrow," said Jimmy.

"I think they will," she said.

That afternoon it began to rain. The sea looked grey and rough. The sky grew darker and darker and a strong wind came up. The waves crashed against the rocks.

Jimmy and his dad worked in the store all day. At supper time they ran from the store to the house.

"I think we're in for a bad storm, Brad," said Margaret. "I just heard on the radio that small boats have to head for shore right away."

"Do you think Terry and his uncle are anywhere near here?" asked Jimmy.

"I hope not," said his dad. "Don't worry about them. They have likely gone into port down the coast."

For a long time Jimmy looked out the window. He saw some small boats hurrying to get to port safely. Some of the big boats didn't seem to be moving.

Mr. Carson handed Jimmy a pair of field glasses. "Take a look at that oil tanker," said his dad. "It's going to ride out the storm."

"The waves are going right over the bow," said Jimmy. "Do you think there will be a shipwreck tonight, Dad?"

"No," said his dad. "They'll see the light from the new lighthouses along the coast."

That night in bed, Jimmy could hear the rain splashing on the window and the waves crashing on the big rocks. The wind howled around the old lighthouse. He thought about Terry and his uncle. He hoped they were safe. Jimmy went to sleep thinking about all the people out in their boats in the storm.

When he woke up the next morning, the sun was shining. The storm was over.

The Storm Bird

Jimmy took a walk down to the little dock where his dad kept their boat. He went there every morning to feed the gulls. He was glad to see that the storm had not smashed the dock or their boat. When he got to the dock he saw a gull lying on the rocks. It was nearly covered with sand. It was moving, but just a little bit. Jimmy knew it was hurt. He ran back to the house and told his mother about the bird.

Margaret got a big box and brought it down to the dock. "I guess the gull was hurt in the storm," she said. She lifted it carefully into the box.

"Do you think it's going to die?" asked Jimmy.

"I don't know," answered his mother. "We can try and look after it."

Jimmy carried the box back to the house. He put it down just outside the back door. Then he put a little dish of water in the box. He put some bread near the bird to see if it would eat. In a few minutes his dad came to look at it.

"I think you should leave it here to rest quietly," said his dad. "Come and help me in the store for a while."

Jimmy went to the store with his dad. He tried not to think about the bird. He could hear the other gulls calling as they flew around the rocks looking for food. Inside the store there were quite a few people to talk to. Jimmy was glad about that.

Jimmy's mother came into the store. "Jimmy," she whispered, "come outside. I have some bad news for you. It's about the gull."

He stepped outside the door with his mother. He knew what she was going to say. "Did it die?" he asked.

"Yes," said his mother. "It was hurt very badly."

"I'll bury it, Mom," said Jimmy. He could feel tears coming into his eyes.

"Do you want me to help?" his mother asked.

"No," said Jimmy. "I can do it."

Jimmy walked over to the bird. It looked peaceful and still. He brushed some of the sand off the bird. Then he dug a hole right near the back door. He buried the gull and put some shells on its grave.

Then he went down to the rocky shore and looked at the sea. Last night it had been wild, rough and angry. Today the waves glittered in the sunlight as they broke against the shore.

Just then, Jimmy heard someone calling his name. He looked over to the dock. He saw a boat coming in. His friend Terry was waving at him and calling, ''Jimmy! Jimmy!''

Jimmy ran to the dock. He was glad to see Terry and his uncle. They were bringing their boat in to the dock.

"Hi, Jimmy," said Terry. "I've got a lot to tell you. I think we had a lucky escape last night. We got to shore just in time. You should have seen the waves. I was really scared."

"Me, too," said Jimmy. "I'm really glad to see you. And do you know what? Mom and Dad said you and your uncle can stay with us for a few days."

"Great!" yelled Terry. "I'll race you to the lighthouse."

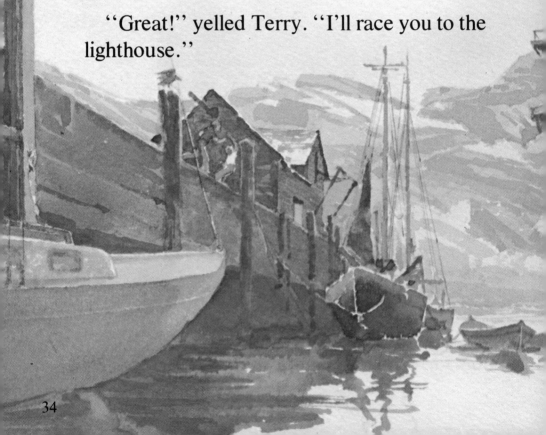

Big White Bird

Big white bird,
Where do you fly?
    Over the clouds,
    Away up high.
And what is there
For you to see?
    The very top
    Of the tall pine tree
    That grows alone
    At the edge of the sea.
Big white bird,
Now where will you go?
    Over the waves,
    Where the wild winds blow.

Wayne Carley

I'd Like to Be a Lighthouse

I'd like to be a lighthouse
    And scrubbed and painted white.

I'd like to be a lighthouse
  And stay awake all night

To keep my eye on everything
  That sails my patch of sea;

I'd like to be a lighthouse
   With the ships all watching me.

Rachel Field

Betsy and the Ghost

Fun and Games

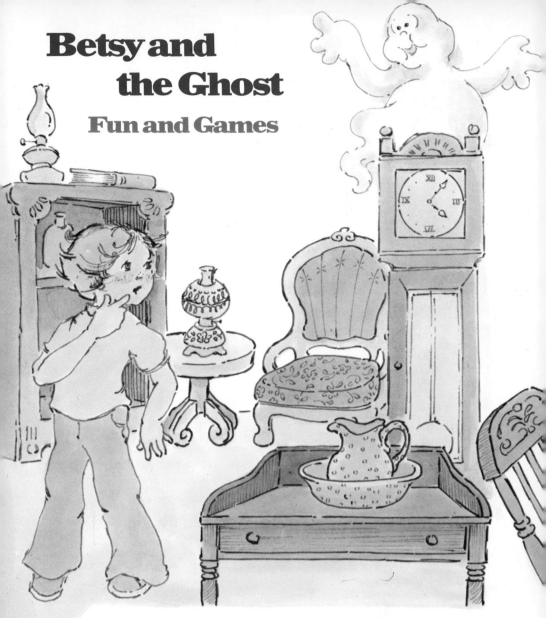

There once was a little girl called Elizabeth Annabel Susan Morningstar. Now that was a very long name for such a little girl, so everyone just called her Betsy.

Every day after school, Betsy went to her grandfather's antique store. It was such an interesting place. There were old tables and old chairs, old pictures and old books in it. There were all kinds of old things. No wonder Betsy thought that her grandfather's shop was the most interesting place she knew.

One day when Betsy went into the shop, she didn't see her grandfather. "Hello, Grandfather," she called. "Where are you?"

There was no answer, so Betsy called again. "Is there anyone here?" she asked.

A high, squeaky voice answered, "No!"

Betsy knew that it wasn't her grandfather's voice. "Who's there?" she called.

"No one," said the squeaky voice, just behind her. Betsy turned around. There, sitting on top of the old grandfather's clock, was a little white ghost.

"Don't be afraid," said the ghost. "I want to be your friend. My name is Oliver."

"Are you a real ghost?" asked Betsy.

"Of course I am," replied the ghost. "Are you a real girl?"

"Oh, yes," said Betsy with a laugh.

"I've never met a real girl before," said Oliver. "Would you like to play with me?"

"I might, if I knew what ghosts played," answered Betsy.

"We play a game called Follow-the-leader," said the ghost.

"That might be very interesting," said Betsy. "You go first and I'll follow you."

Oliver jumped down from the grandfather's clock and moved around the shop. Betsy followed him. He climbed over a table and under a chair. Betsy did that, too. Then Oliver went through a door without even opening it.

"Come back, please," called Betsy, "I can't do that."

"I'm sorry," said Oliver as he came back through the door. "Now you will be the leader. I'll follow you for a while."

Betsy turned around three times. She jumped over an armchair and ran around the table. Oliver followed her. She picked up a book and put it down. Then she opened a window and shut it again. The little ghost did everything that Betsy did. When she took off her shoes and put them on again, Oliver looked sad.

"I'm sorry," said Betsy. "I forgot that you didn't have shoes. Maybe we should play another game."

"What game do you want to play?" asked Oliver.

"Let's play Hide-and-seek," replied Betsy. "That's a good game."

"I know it is. We ghosts play Hide-and-seek most of the time," said Oliver. "You hide first and I'll shut my eyes."

Oliver shut his eyes. Betsy got under the table. "Ready or not, you will be caught," called the ghost in a squeaky voice. Then he flew around the room. When he saw Betsy under the table, he said, "One-two-three, I see you. Now you're *It* and it's my turn to hide."

This time Betsy shut her eyes. "Ready or not, you will be caught," she called. "Here I come."

First Betsy looked between two boxes. Then she looked in the big armchair, behind all the pictures, and inside the old grandfather's clock. She couldn't find the ghost anywhere.

"Where are you?" she called.

Oliver didn't answer. All at once Betsy heard a squeaky laugh coming from the fireplace. She ran across the room and looked up the chimney.

"One-two-three, I see you," she shouted.

The little ghost came down the chimney. He was covered with black spots. Betsy took one look at him and began to laugh. Oliver took one look at Betsy, and he laughed too. She had soot all over her face.

"I hope this soot will come off," said Oliver. "I don't want to be a spotted ghost."

"Come here," said Betsy. "I'll help you. I'll blow the soot away." She blew and blew and blew.

"Kerchoo! Kerchoo!" sneezed the ghost. "That tickles my nose," he said.

"Now you help me," said Betsy. She shut her eyes while the ghost blew the soot off her face. When she opened her eyes, the ghost wasn't there.

Just then, in walked her grandfather. "Hello, Betsy," he said. "Was there anyone in the shop while I was out?"

"Yes," she answered. "A friend of mine was here, but he left in a hurry."

"Where did he go?" asked her grandfather.

"I forgot to ask him," replied Betsy.

"I'm sorry that I didn't get back in time to meet him," said her grandfather.

"I'm sorry, too," said Betsy, "but he might come back some other time."

"I hope he will," said her grandfather.

Just then, Elizabeth Annabel Susan Morningstar thought she heard a high squeaky laugh coming from inside the grandfather's clock. But she wasn't sure.

Tiger by the Tail

It was spring. It was Saturday. It was sunny and warm. And Betsy Morningstar felt happy.

"I think I'll go visit Grandfather in his store," Betsy said to herself.

Her grandfather wasn't the only person Betsy was going to visit. She was going to visit the ghost who lived in the old clock in her grandfather's store. Betsy giggled to herself. "I bet I'm the only person in the whole city who knows a ghost."

Betsy was becoming very good friends with the ghost. She and Oliver spent hours together playing in the store. They thought that an antique store was more fun than anywhere else.

Betsy ran into the shop. "Hello, Grandfather," she called.

"Oh, Betsy, I'm glad you're here," said her grandfather. "Will you please look after the shop for a little while? I have to deliver the chair I sold yesterday."

"Of course I will," said Betsy. "I like looking after the store."

"I shouldn't be gone very long," said her grandfather. "If anyone comes in, just tell them I'll be back in half an hour."

When he had gone, Betsy went over to Oliver's clock.

"Oliver! Oliver! Come out and play," she called.

Oliver answered, "I'll come out, but I won't play. I don't feel like playing today."

"Oh, Oliver," said Betsy. "What's wrong with you today?"

"I don't like living with all this junk around me," Oliver answered.

"It's not junk," said Betsy. "Everything in this store is an antique."

"It's junk," said Oliver, flying out of the clock. He flew around the store. "Just look at this old stuff. Who would want it?"

"Lots of people," said Betsy. "Everything in this store is over a hundred years old."

"So what? So am I!" answered Oliver.

"I dare you to show me one piece of junk in this store," said Betsy.

"This is junk," said Oliver as he sat down in an old rocking chair and began to rock.

"Ha!" said Betsy. "That's all you know. That just happens to be the chair Laura Secord sat in every night after she brought her cows home. It's worth a lot of money."

Oliver flew around the store.

"I've found something that really is junk," he cried.

Betsy followed him to a dusty corner of the store. Oliver was holding an old grey teapot. Betsy wondered if Oliver was right. Maybe it was just a piece of junk. She picked up the teapot.

"I bet this teapot is made of silver," she said. "All it needs is to be cleaned up." She began to rub it on her T-shirt.

VOOM! All at once a huge cloud of smoke came out of the teapot. Betsy and Oliver both cried out. Soon the smoke began to clear.

"What is your wish, little one?" said a voice from the smoke.

Oliver darted about in fear. "Betsy! What is it?"

"I d-d-d-don't know," said Betsy. "But I think it's a genie."

"What's a genie?" asked Oliver.

Just then the smoke cleared away. A tall man in a turban stood in front of them.

"I am the genie of the Silver Teapot, and I will give you two wishes."

"Anything?" asked Oliver, flying around excitedly.

"Anything at all!" said the genie.

"Oh, hurray!" shouted Oliver without thinking. "I want to be a tiger. I've always wanted to be a tiger."

VOOM! The genie disappeared. Oliver was a tiger — a huge orange and black striped Bengal tiger.

"Oliver! You come out of there at once," shouted Betsy.

The tiger roared and flicked his tail.

Just then the door of the store opened. "Quick!" whispered Betsy. "Someone is coming in. Lie on the floor and look like a rug."

"Is anyone here?" a voice called.

"Yes, I'm here," said Betsy. "I'm here. May I help you?"

"I was just doing my shopping and I thought I'd drop in," said a woman. "I know you won't have it, but I'll ask anyway. I'm looking for a bearskin rug. They are very hard to find these days."

"No, I'm sorry. We don't have any. Good day," said Betsy, trying to hurry the woman out of the store.

"Well, while I'm here, I'll just look around," said the woman.

"I'm sorry," said Betsy. "You'll have to go. It's closing time."

"But it's only eleven o'clock in the morning," said the woman.

"I know, but we have to close because I have to go to the dentist," said Betsy.
Oliver laughed, but it came out as a roar.

"What was that?" cried the woman.

"Just my kitten," answered Betsy. "She has a very loud purr."

Just then the woman spotted Oliver. "Oh! A tiger-skin rug," she said. "I've always wanted one. How much is it?" She put her grocery bag down beside the rug.

"It's not for sale," said Betsy. "Now I really have to close."

"Are you sure it's not for sale?" the woman asked. "I'll pay a lot of money for it."

"It's not a very good rug," said Betsy. She heard a crunching sound. She looked down. Oliver was eating the woman's groceries.

"My groceries!" screamed the woman.

Betsy said, "Well, I told you it wasn't a very good rug. It isn't housebroken yet."

"It's alive!" screamed the woman. "Get me out of here. You'd better come with me, little girl. That thing could eat us both."

She pulled Betsy toward the door.

"Oliver! Oliver!" Betsy cried.

The tiger came after them. The woman pulled Betsy out into the street and slammed the door.

"I'll go for help!" said the woman. She ran down the street.

As soon as the woman was around the corner, Betsy went back into the store. Oliver was sitting in the rocking chair, smiling and licking his tail.

Betsy pretended to be angry. "That's not very funny," she said. Then they both burst out laughing.

"How do we get out of this mess?" asked Betsy. "She'll be back any minute. What do we do?"

"I guess I'll have to use my other wish," said Oliver. "I've been a tiger long enough."

"Hurry up, Oliver," said Betsy. "Someone is coming. Make the other wish. I hope the genie can hear you."

VOOM! Oliver was himself again.

Just then, Betsy's grandfather rushed into the store. "Betsy! Betsy! Are you all right?" he called.

"Of course I'm all right, Grandfather."

Betsy's grandfather said, "Thank goodness. I met a woman down the street who said there was a tiger running around in my store."

"That's silly!" said Betsy.

"That's what I told the policeman," said her grandfather.

"I'll just dust this grandfather's clock," said Betsy. She opened the door and tickled Oliver with her feather duster.

"Kerchoo!" said Oliver.

"Bless you," said Betsy's grandfather.

Betsy giggled. Then she said, "Tomorrow I'll finish cleaning this old teapot, Grandfather."

"All right," said her grandfather, "but I don't think anyone will ever buy it. It's just a piece of junk."

My Grandfather's Clock

My grandfather's clock was too large for the shelf,
So it stood ninety years on the floor.
It was taller by half than the old man himself,
Though it weighed not a pennyweight more.
It was bought on the morn of the day that he was born,
And was always his treasure and pride.
But it stopped short, never to go again,
When the old man died.

Ninety years without slumbering,
Tick-tock! Tick-tock!
His life's seconds numbering,
Tick-tock! Tick-tock!
It stopped short, never to go again
When the old man died.

Henry C. Work

Dear Uncle Doug,

Thank you for the old music box you sent me when I was sick. It makes me feel happy. ←ME

I'd like to visit your antique shop this Saturday. Is it O.K. if my friends and come too?

Rebecca   Caitlin

　　　Your BIG nephew,
　　　Frank

Come In

. . . and Make Believe

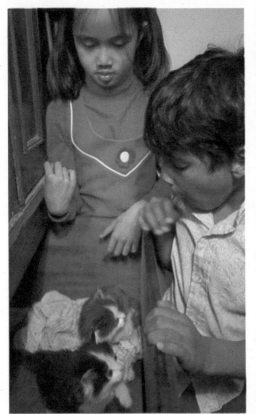
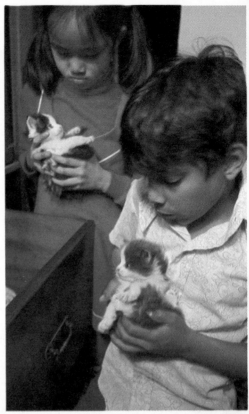

The Owl and the Pussy-Cat

The Owl and the Pussy-Cat went to sea
    In a beautiful pea-green boat:
They took some honey, and plenty of money,
    Wrapped up in a five-pound note.
The Owl looked up to the stars above,
    And sang to a small guitar,
"O lovely Pussy! O Pussy, my love,
    What a beautiful Pussy you are,
        You are,
        You are!
    What a beautiful Pussy you are!"

JONATHAN MILNE

Pussy said to the Owl, "You elegant fowl,
How charmingly sweet you sing!
Oh! let us be married; too long we have tarried:
But what shall we do for a ring?"
They sailed away, for a year and a day,
To the land where the Bong tree grows;
And there in a wood a Piggy-wig stood,
With a ring at the end of his nose,
His nose,
His nose,
With a ring at the end of his nose.

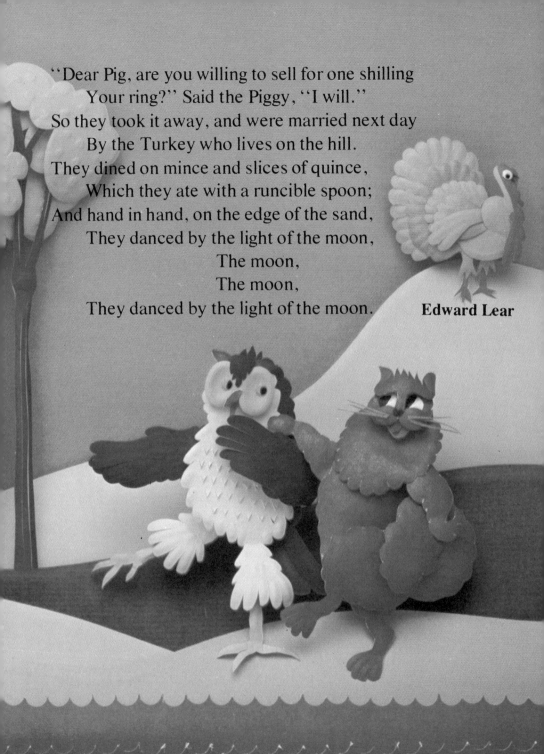

"Dear Pig, are you willing to sell for one shilling
    Your ring?" Said the Piggy, "I will."
So they took it away, and were married next day
    By the Turkey who lives on the hill.
They dined on mince and slices of quince,
    Which they ate with a runcible spoon;
And hand in hand, on the edge of the sand,
    They danced by the light of the moon,
            The moon,
            The moon,
    They danced by the light of the moon.

Edward Lear

The Elves and the Shoemakers

PEOPLE IN THE PLAY

Gustav

Hilda

A Rich Man

The First Princess

The Second Princess

A Young Man

The Blue Elf

The Red Elf

The Green Elf

The Brown Elf

The play takes place in the shoemakers' shop.

Act One

Scene One

Time: Late one evening.

> (*GUSTAV is sitting at the table looking into a money-box. HILDA comes into the room holding a lamp.*)

GUSTAV: Hilda, we are growing poorer and poorer every day. Soon all our money will be gone. We must make some shoes to sell.

HILDA: There are only four pieces of silver left in the money-box. That's not enough money to buy food for our family. They will soon go hungry.

GUSTAV: It isn't even enough money to buy leather to make shoes.

HILDA: How much leather is left?

GUSTAV: Just this one piece.

(GUSTAV holds up one piece of leather.)

HILDA: It's not very good leather, but perhaps there's enough to make one pair of shoes. Let's start work on them tonight.

GUSTAV: It's getting late. I'll light the lamp so that we can see to work.

HILDA: Thank you, Gustav. Now it is time the children were in bed. Will you come up and say goodnight to them?

GUSTAV: Yes, and I'll tell them a story, too. But first I'll cut out this leather.

HILDA: I don't know what will become of us when our last pieces of money are gone.

GUSTAV: We cannot make shoes to sell if we do not have leather. We cannot buy leather if we have no money. What will become of us?

(HILDA goes out. GUSTAV begins to cut the leather.)

Scene Two

Time: The next morning.

GUSTAV: Come quickly, Hilda. See what has happened! I can't believe my eyes!

(HILDA comes hurrying into the room.)

GUSTAV: Last evening we cut out the leather for a pair of shoes, but we didn't sew them. This morning when I came into the room, I found a pair of finished shoes here on the table. Someone must have come into the shop and made the shoes while we were asleep. I can't think who could have done it. Look at these fine stitches.

HILDA: They are beautiful! I never would have believed it! How could anyone make such good-looking shoes from such poor leather? See how the leather shines. They will bring a good price.

GUSTAV: I'll put them in the window at once for everyone to see. If we sell them, we'll have money to buy some food for our children. We might have enough money to buy more leather, too.

HILDA: I'll clean up the shop as quickly as I can.

(GUSTAV gets the window ready and puts the shoes in it. HILDA works around the shop.)

GUSTAV: Hilda, people are already stopping to look at the shoes. I hope someone will come in to ask about them.

HILDA: There's a tall man coming to the door. He is wearing fine clothes. He must be very rich. Maybe he will like the shoes and buy them.

(The RICH MAN opens the door and comes into the shop.)

RICH MAN: Good day, my friends. You have a pair of fine shoes in the window. How much do they cost?

GUSTAV: They cost twenty pieces of silver.

RICH MAN: Only twenty pieces of silver! That is a very fair price. May I try them on?

GUSTAV: Of course. Sit down in this chair, sir. I'll get them out of the window for you.

(GUSTAV gets the shoes and helps the RICH MAN try them on.)

RICH MAN: They fit very well. I'll buy them.

HILDA: I'll put them in a box for you.

RICH MAN: I shall tell all my friends about the fine shoes you make.

(The RICH MAN counts out the money and gives it to HILDA.)

HILDA: Thank you, sir, and good day to you.

(The RICH MAN takes the box and leaves the shop.)

HILDA: Twenty pieces of silver! That's enough to buy bread and milk for our children.

GUSTAV: And leather for two more pairs of shoes. Let's go to the leather shop at once to buy some.

HILDA: And on the way back, we can buy food at the market.

GUSTAV: Tonight after supper we can cut out two more pairs of shoes. Tomorrow we can sew them. Just think, only last night we didn't know what would become of us. Now we have money to buy food and more leather. Whoever made those shoes has done us a good turn.

Scene Three

Time: The next morning.

HILDA: I can't believe my eyes! Last night we cut out the leather and left it on the table. This morning there are two pairs of pretty red dancing-shoes.

GUSTAV: The sewing has been done with great care. Every stitch is in place.

HILDA: The shoes are as light as feathers. See how they shine in the sunlight.

GUSTAV: Whoever made these shoes is a very fine shoemaker. I wonder who it can be.

(HILDA puts the dancing-shoes in the window. She looks out the window at the street.)

HILDA: It is only nine o'clock, and already there are many people out shopping. Look! A beautiful carriage pulled by two fine black horses has stopped outside our shop.

GUSTAV: There's a man getting out of the carriage. He's coming over to the window.

HILDA: Now he's going back to the carriage, and he's opening the door.

GUSTAV: Would you believe it! Two young princesses are getting out of the carriage and they are looking in our shop window. They are coming to the door!

HILDA: Princesses coming into our shop! We must not keep them waiting. Hurry! Let them in!

(GUSTAV goes to the door and opens it. The TWO PRINCESSES enter the shop.)

FIRST PRINCESS: Good morning. We have heard about the fine shoes you sell.

SECOND PRINCESS: Everyone at the palace is talking about them.

(GUSTAV and HILDA bow to the PRINCESSES.)

GUSTAV: Good morning, Princesses. Thank you for your kind words.

FIRST PRINCESS: We have been looking at the red dancing-shoes in your window.

SECOND PRINCESS: We would like to try them on. We'll buy them if they fit.

HILDA: Would you care to sit here while I get them for you?

(The PRINCESSES sit down. GUSTAV and HILDA go to the window. They get the shoes and help the PRINCESSES put them on.)

FIRST PRINCESS: These shoes are as soft as kittens' fur and as light as feathers. They fit me very well.

SECOND PRINCESS: You would think that this pair had been made just for me. I would like to wear them to the ball tonight. How much do they cost?

FIRST PRINCESS: We'll take them, no matter what they cost.

GUSTAV: We are asking twenty pieces of silver for each pair.

SECOND PRINCESS: That is a very fair price. We will take them.

(GUSTAV and HILDA put the shoes in boxes and give them to the PRINCESSES. Each PRINCESS gives them a bag of money. The PRINCESSES leave the shop.)

HILDA: We are no longer poor. We have money to buy even more leather than before, and enough food to last us all week.

GUSTAV: Remember the last time we were in the leather shop? We saw two fine pieces of leather. We could make four pairs of boots with it. The leather costs only twelve pieces of silver.

HILDA: We should go to the leather shop at once and buy it.

GUSTAV: When we come home, we'll be able to cut out the leather for the boots.

HILDA: Our children will be happy when they see what good things we bring home from the market.

GUSTAV: I can't believe that all this money is ours. Whoever made these shoes has been very kind to us.

(*GUSTAV and HILDA leave the shop.*)

Scene Four

Time: The following morning.

GUSTAV: Hilda, it has happened again! Last
evening we cut out the leather, just as we
said we would. This morning I have found
four pairs of riding-boots on the table.

HILDA: Riding-boots! What handsome ones
they are!

GUSTAV: See how well the stitching has been
done. It would take us weeks to make
boots like these. It seems impossible that
all these boots have been made in just one
night.

HILDA: It seems like magic. Last night we left
the pieces of leather here, and this
morning we have the finished boots.

GUSTAV: Such fine boots should sell quickly.

HILDA: Let's put them in the window at once.

*(GUSTAV and HILDA put the boots in the
window. The sound of a galloping horse
can be heard outside. The sound stops.)*

HILDA: A young man on horseback has stopped in front of our shop. He's getting off his horse and coming to look in our window. He seems to be interested in the riding-boots.

(The YOUNG MAN enters the shop.)

YOUNG MAN: Good morning. Those riding-boots in the window are very handsome.

GUSTAV: Thank you, sir. I'll bring you a pair so that you may have a better look at them.

(GUSTAV gives the YOUNG MAN one pair of boots.)

YOUNG MAN: I can see that they are well made from the very best leather.

GUSTAV: Would you like to buy a pair of these boots?

YOUNG MAN: I would like to buy eight pairs. Do you have that many?

GUSTAV: Eight pairs! I am sorry, sir, but we have only four pairs in the shop.

YOUNG MAN: I will take them and come back for more in a few weeks.

GUSTAV: May I ask if you are buying all these boots for yourself?

YOUNG MAN: No, they are for the king's horsemen to wear. The king is willing to pay five pieces of gold for each pair. Is that enough?

GUSTAV: That's a very good price. We would be very pleased to have the king's horsemen wearing boots from our shop.

(The YOUNG MAN counts out twenty pieces of gold. He gives them to GUSTAV. He takes the boots and leaves the shop.)

HILDA: Twenty pieces of gold! We are rich!

GUSTAV: Just a few days ago we were poor. Now we have enough money to last us a long time. I'll go to the leather shop before supper and buy enough leather to make four more pairs of boots.

HILDA: Why don't you buy some very soft leather to make some children's shoes, too?

GUSTAV: That's a good idea. We don't need to make the riding boots for a few weeks. We can cut out the leather for the children's shoes tonight.

HILDA: I wish we could thank whoever helped us make the boots and shoes.

GUSTAV: I have a plan. After supper, when the children are in bed, we can cut out the leather. Then we'll stay up to watch what happens. We can hide behind the door.

HILDA: We can leave the lantern on the table. We will be able to see who is doing all this work for us.

Act Two
Scene One

Time: Later that night.

> *(GUSTAV and HILDA are waiting behind the door.)*

HILDA: It's nearly twelve o'clock. I thought that someone would have come by now. I think we should go to bed.

GUSTAV: No, let's wait until twelve o'clock.

HILDA: Shhh! There is someone at the door.

> *(The door opens. The BLUE ELF enters and looks around, then goes back to the door and gives a whistle.)*

BLUE ELF: No one is here. It's safe to come in.

(One by one, three other ELVES enter.)

BROWN ELF: I see that the shoemakers have left us our leather again tonight. The first night we came, there were only a few pieces of very poor leather. Every night after that there has been more and better leather.

RED ELF: There are more pieces than ever tonight! The shoemakers must have sold all the shoes we made for them.

BLUE ELF: These pieces of leather are very small. We'll make them into children's shoes.

GREEN ELF: The leather is as soft as can be.

BROWN ELF: Perhaps the shoemakers will give a pair of shoes to each of their children.

RED ELF: We must make them with great care.

(The ELVES begin to work on the leather.)

BLUE ELF: Do you think it's safe for us to sing?

GREEN ELF: I'm sure it is. Everyone in the house must be sleeping by now.

RED ELF: When we sing, the time seems to go quickly and the work goes well.

GREEN ELF: Let's sing our stitching song. That's the one I like best.

BROWN ELF: I like that song, too.

FOUR ELVES: Stitch and sew.
Stitch and sew.
See how fast
The minutes go.
Stitch and sew.
Sew for fun.
See how fast
The work is done.

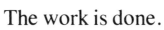

RED ELF: I have finished a pair of shoes already. Singing our song helped me.

BROWN ELF: Look at this pair. Some little child will like to dance about in these.

BLUE ELF: I have put leather bows on these shoes.

BROWN ELF: They are pretty. Now we must work quickly to finish the other shoes.

GREEN ELF: Let's sing again. When we do, the work seems to go faster.

FOUR ELVES: Stitch and sew.
Sew with care.
See how well
We make each pair.
Stitch and sew.
Sew for fun.
Four new pairs
At last are done.

BLUE ELF: Our work is finished already. It's time for us to go. We'll come back tomorrow night at twelve o'clock.

(The ELVES go out. GUSTAV and HILDA come out from behind the door.)

GUSTAV: I can hardly believe it! To think that all those beautiful shoes and boots have been made by four elves!

HILDA: Look at the pretty little children's shoes that they have made tonight. Have you ever seen such fine work?

GUSTAV: How can we ever thank the elves for all they have done for us?

HILDA: I think I know how we can thank them. Did you see what poor clothes the elves were wearing? I don't know how they keep themselves warm. We could make some new clothes for them.

GUSTAV: Yes, let's do that. We can make new coats and hats for them, and some little boots and warm mittens as well.

Scene Two

Time: A few evenings later.

> *(GUSTAV and HILDA are busy working at the table.)*

GUSTAV: I've just finished the last leather mitten. Is everything ready now, Hilda?

HILDA: I'll be finished in a minute or two. I have just a few stitches left to sew. I hope the elves like their new clothes.

GUSTAV: I'm glad that we have been able to do something for them.

HILDA: There now, I've finished the last stitch. We'll put the clothes here on the table.

GUSTAV: I'll put the lantern beside the clothes. Then the elves will see them when they come into the shop. We must hurry. It's nearly twelve o'clock, and the elves will be here in a few minutes.

HILDA: Won't they be surprised when they see the clothes! I wonder what they will say.

GUSTAV: Shhh! I hear a sound outside. We must hide at once. Hurry! Get behind the door. We don't want them to see us.

(*GUSTAV and HILDA hide. The GREEN ELF comes in, looks around, and gives a whistle. The other ELVES enter.*)

BROWN ELF: I wonder how many pieces of leather the shoemakers have left on the table.

BLUE ELF: Each night there have been more and better pieces for us to sew.

RED ELF: That's funny! Tonight there's no leather.

BROWN ELF: Perhaps the shoemakers forgot to leave it.

BLUE ELF: But look! They have left us
    something in place of the leather.

GREEN ELF: They have left us some new
    clothes!

RED ELF: This red coat and hat must be for
    me. They will keep me warm.

GREEN ELF: There are coats and hats for us
    all.

(The ELVES try on the clothes.)

BLUE ELF: See how well this blue coat fits
    me. I'm going to wear it all the time.

BROWN ELF: What fine boots they have made
    for us!

GREEN ELF: There are mittens here, too.
Now our hands will be warm when we
play in the snow.

BROWN ELF: Let's sing a song about our new
clothes. *(The ELVES dance as they sing.)*

FOUR ELVES: Stitch and sew.
Stitch and sew.
To all our friends,
Our clothes we'll show.
Stitch and sew.
Stitch and sew.
We like it here,
We'll never go.

The End

Editors

Ruta Demery
Clayton Graves

Language Arts Consultants

Mimi Garry
Margaret Turner

Photos

page 36	Miller Services
page 37	G.H. Graham,
page 38	Miller Services
page 39	E. Otto,
	Miller Services

Film

Colourgraph

Printing

McLaren, Morris & Todd

© Thomas Nelson and Sons
(Canada) Limited 1977

Acknowledgements

Grateful acknowledgement is made to the following for permission to reprint the material indicated.

"I'd Like to Be a Lighthouse", Copyright 1926 by Doubleday and Company, Inc. from *Taxis and Toadstools* by Rachel Field. Reprinted by permission of the publisher.

Wayne Carley for "Betsy and the Ghost".

John McInnes for "Mr. and Mrs. Impossible", and "Summer at Rocky Point".

ISBN: 0-17-600572-2

11 12 13 14 15   MMT   8 7 6 5 4 3